The winds of political change blow strong and strange in this latest serving of DOONESBURY adventures. Freshly franchised Congresswoman Lacey Davenport arrives in Washington with her ornithologist husband, and, with the unlikely staff support of law graduate Joanie Caucus, plunges into the Korean Lobby investigation. Uncle Duke is phased out of his envoyship to China, determined not to understand what Leonard Woodcock may have that he doesn't. And the new administration adds to the cabinet a Secretary of Symbolism, whose string of coups (the call-in show, the limo cuts, Amy's ''trusty'' governess, etc.) is capped by the first annual Human Rights Awards Banquet. Once again, no one is spared in what may well be the choicest collection by the only comic strip cartoonist ever to win the Pulitzer Prize.

DOONESBURY

The remarkable comic strip called DOONESBURY has provoked more public and media reaction than any cartoon in the last twenty-five years, winning legions of loyal followers. Michael J. Doonesbury and the denizens of Walden Commune appear in nearly five hundred newspapers with a readership of over 23 million.

"You know for certain that a journalist is influential when he's a step ahead of the White House, when his ideas are being co-opted by the Administration as its own. So it is with Trudeau."

—*New Republic*

Bantam Books by G.B. Trudeau
Ask your bookseller for the books you have missed

Stalking the Perfect Tan

a Doonesbury book

by G. B. Trudeau

BANTAM BOOKS
TORONTO • NEW YORK • LONDON

STALKING THE PERFECT TAN
*A Bantam Book / published by arrangement with
Holt, Rinehart & Winston*

PRINTING HISTORY
*Holt, Rinehart & Winston edition published March 1978
3 printings through August 1978*

Bantam edition / March 1981

ISBN 0-553-14796-X

Published simultaneously in the United States and Canada

PRINTED IN THE UNITED STATES OF AMERICA

0 9 8 7 6 5 4 3 2 1

I REALLY DON'T UNDERSTAND WHY YOU'RE SO KEEN ON GOING TO THIS PARTY, LACEY..
WELL, FOR ONE THING, DICK, THE ENTIRE CARTER CABINET WILL PROBABLY BE THERE!
THAT'S A DRAW?! THE CARTER CABINET IS THE MOST BIZARRE COL-LECTION OF CRONIES, RETREADS AND TOKENS EVER ASSEMBLED!
I KNOW THAT, DEAR, BUT I'M NEW IN TOWN! I WANT A CHANCE TO SIZE UP THE PEOPLE IN CHARGE!
OKAY, BUT WHY DO I HAVE TO GO? WHO'S GOING TO WANT TO TALK TO AN ELDERLY ORNITHOLOGIST?
ME. IN 35 YEARS, I'VE NEVER BEEN TO A PARTY WHERE YOU WEREN'T THE MOST FASCINATING PERSON THERE.
OH.
KEEP YOUR EYES ON THE ROAD, DRIVER.
YES'M.
GBTrudeau

A FINAL WORD TO THE WISE, EVERYONE: WHEN REPORTING SALARIES, ALWAYS TELL IT LIKE IT IS! IT'S TIME WE STOPPED USING EUPHEMISMS LIKE "A SIX-FIGURE INCOME"!
MEDIA
MEDIA
LET'S SAY YOUR SUBJECT EARNS "A SIX-FIGURE INCOME". DOES THAT MEAN HE MAKES $100,000, OR $900,000? THIS IS A VERY IMPORTANT DISTINCTION TO OUR READERS!
MEDIA
I SAY, LET'S CALL A $100,000 SALARY $100,000, AND A $900,000 SALARY $900,000!
HEAR! HEAR!
YEEAA! YEA!
CLAP! CLAP! CLAP! CLAP!
MEDIA
THANK YOU. I'VE BEEN ASKED TO REMIND YOU THAT THE JACKIE O. RETROSPECTIVE WILL RESUME AT THREE.
WE'LL BE COVERING THE GREEK YEARS TODAY, PEOPLE!
MEDIA
©GBTrudeau

ANY OTHER QUESTIONS?
YES, WHAT DO YOU THINK OF GAME SHOW CELE-BRITIES?
WELL, AS YOU KNOW, GAME SHOW CELEBRITIES ARE NOT REALLY CELEBRITIES IN ANY FORMAL SENSE, SINCE FEW OF THEM HAVE EVER DONE ANYTHING WORTH CELEBRATING!
IT'S A NECESSARY SYSTEM, THOUGH. ONLY BY CREATING THEIR OWN "CELEBRITIES" CAN MOST GAME SHOWS STAY IN THE BLACK!
WELL, WHERE DO THEY GET THESE PEOPLE?
BURBANK. AS I UN-DERSTAND IT, THEY'RE RAISED IN ABANDONED SOUND STAGES..
MEOW, MEOW!
G.B. Trudeau

RICK, HAVE YOU WORKED UP THIS WEEK'S GOSSIP FOR "CHATTER" YET?
OH, C'MON, BRENDA, YOU DON'T REALLY EXPECT ME TO HANDLE THAT PAGE, DO YOU?
I CERTAINLY DO! LISTEN, RICK, THIS MAGAZINE ONLY SERVICES ONE NEED, AND THAT'S ENTERTAINMENT! WE DON'T MAKE CLAIMS TO PROVIDE ANYTHING ELSE!
NO ONE MADE YOU TAKE THIS JOB, SO YOU CAN JUST STOP BEING SO DAMN CONDESCENDING! NOW, I WANT THOSE ITEMS TODAY, OKAY?!
ALL RIGHT, ALL RIGHT...
AND I WANT THEM JUICY, RICK!
I HEAR YOU, BRENDA..
© BTrudeau

HEY, JIM— YOU GETTIN' EXCITED ABOUT THE KID YET?
YEAH, I GUESS I AM, BOB. BUT I FEEL SO UNPREPARED, YOU KNOW? I MEAN, WHAT AM I GOING TO DO WITH A KID?
GIVE HIM A GUITAR, MAN. HE'LL HAVE THE GENES..
NO, NO, I PROMISED MYSELF I WOULDN'T PUSH THE MUSIC. IT'S NOT FAIR!
HE'S GOT THE APTITUDE, THOUGH. HE ALREADY SOUNDS LIKE A WHOLE RHYTHM SECTION. IT'S DRIVING JENNY CRAZY!
HEY, KID! BE SMART, KID!
BOOM-CHUCKA! BOOM-CHUCKA!
ROOTS
GB Trudeau

HI, JEN.. SORRY I'M LATE.
THAT'S OKAY. OUR BUDDING PERCUSSIONIST HAS KEPT ME GROUNDED ANYWAY..
ROOTS
HE'S BEEN ACTING UP AGAIN?
HEAR FOR YOURSELF. THE NEXT SHOW IS JUST BEGINNING.
BOOM! BOOM!
ROOTS
WHA?..
BOOM-CHUCKA! BOOM-CHUCKA!
ROOTS
GOOD **LORD!** THE KID'S GOT A **BACK-BEAT!**
IT'S JUST AGGRAVATION TO ME!
DIPPITY-DIP-DIP! SHUSH! BAM!
ROOTS
GBTrudeau

JIMMY, GUESS WHAT HAPPENED THIS AFTERNOON! I HAD MY FIRST BRAXTON-HICKS CONTRACTIONS!
YOU DID?
UH-HUH! ISN'T IT EXCITING?
JENNY, WHAT ARE BRAXTON-HICKS CONTRACTIONS?
THEY'RE PRELIMINARY CONTRACTIONS, JIMMY! NAMED AFTER THE MAN WHO FORMALLY DESCRIBED THEM IN MEDICAL LITERATURE!
OH, SURE, THAT'S RIGHT..
JIMMY, YOU **PROMISED** TO READ UP ON MY STAGES!
HEY, C'MON, JEN, I'VE BEEN ON THE ROAD!
© GBTrudeau

OKAY, CLASS, LET'S ALL SETTLE DOWN! DR. KISSINGER WILL BE HERE IN A FEW MINUTES!
HEY, MAN, WHY US? I THOUGHT HE WAS BEING FED TO THE GRAD STUDENTS.
WELL, IT SEEMS MOST OF THEM STILL REMEMBER THE TRASHING OF INDOCHINA. IT WAS THOUGHT YOU FRESHMEN MIGHT BE A LITTLE LESS HOSTILE.
SOUND REASONING!
NOT SO! MY OLDER BROTHER TOLD ME ALL ABOUT THE WAR BEFORE HE LEFT TO GROW CABBAGES IN VERMONT!
DON'T WORRY, BARNEY, YOU'RE STILL THE ULTIMATE FRESHMAN.
OKAY, NOW, IF WE COULD ALL JUST SIT UP STRAIGHT..
I AM?
HELL, YES. EVEN I FIND YOU REFRESHING!
GBTrudeau

HELLO? IS ANYONE THERE?
GOOD AFTERNOON, THIS IS "ASK YOUR PRESIDENT"! GO AHEAD, PLEASE!
J. CARTER
IS THIS MY PRESIDENT SPEAKING?
NO, THIS IS WALTER CRONKITE.
J. CARTER
DARN! I URGENTLY NEED TO ASK MY PRESIDENT A QUESTION!
I'M SORRY, SIR, BUT YOU HAVE TO ASK ME FIRST. I'M SCREENING OUT THE NUTS.
J. CARTER
I AM NOT A NUT! WHO SAID I WAS A NUT? IT WAS MOTHER, WASN'T IT!
CLICK!
HELLO? HELLO? AM I ON THE AIR?
UM.. GOOD AFTER-NOON, THIS IS..
J. CARTER
GBTrudeau

OKAY, NOW WHERE IN THE BOOK DO YOU WANT ME TO LOOK?
I THINK IT'S..UM.. CHAPTER SEVEN.
"THIS TIME THE CONTRACTIONS ARE NOT GOING AWAY. TRUE LABOR IS IDENTIFIED BY REG-ULAR CONTRACTIONS WHICH BECOME INCREASINGLY STRONGER..."
THAT'S IT!.. OOH!
THAT'S IT? WHAT DO YOU MEAN, THAT'S IT?
THAT'S WHAT'S HAPPENING, JIMMY.. UNHH! RIGHT NOW.. COULD.. YOU GO GET THE DOCTOR?..
OH, MY GOD!
ZIP!
THANK YOU..
GB Trudeau

UNHH!.. OOOH.. OOOH!..
HEEY...SHE'S A GOOD LITTLE BREATHER!..YOU GUYS ARE INTO LAMAZE, HUH?
YEAH...
YOU KNOW, YOU LOOK VERY FAMILIAR.. AREN'T YOU JIM THUDPUCKER, THE POP STAR?
UUNH.. OOH...
UH-HUH. EASY, JEN!
UUNH.... GASP!.. UUNH!!..
EASY, BABE! EASY!
HEY, YOU KNOW WHAT SONG OF YOURS I REALLY LIKE?..
WILL YOU PAY ATTENTION!
GBTrudeau

UNHH! OOH.. OOH!..
OKAY, BEAU-TIFUL, WE'RE GETTING CLOSE, SO WITH THE NEXT CONTRACTION, I WANT YOU TO PUSH!
OOH! UNHH! OOH!
AS THE CONTRACTION STARTS, TAKE A DEEP BREATH, LET IT OUT; TAKE ANOTHER, LET IT OUT; TAKE ANOTHER, GRASP YOUR KNEES AND BEAR DOWN! OKAY? READY?
WAAAAH!
OH..UM.. NEVER MIND!
JENNY! YOU STAR!
G B Trudeau

OH, RIGHT, ONE OTHER THING, GREG! I'D LIKE TO BEEF UP THE QUOTA OF "AVERAGE AMERICANS" INVITED TO STATE DINNERS TO 20%, OKAY?
WILL DO, DUANE! I'LL BE BACK ATCHA!
CLICK!
BZZ! BZZZ!
WHITE HOUSE SYMBOLS, DELACOURT SPEAKING!
MR. DELACOURT, THIS IS JENNER DOWN AT WARD-ROBE. YOU CALLED ME, SIR?
YEAH, JENNER, ON THE NEXT FIRESIDE CHAT, I'D LIKE TO TRY A LEISURE SUIT ON THE BOSS. IN.. OH.. DACRON, POLYESTER, SOMETHING OF THIS NATURE..
YESSIR! I'LL GET ON IT, SIR!
CLICK!
BZZ! BZZZ!
SYMBOLS, DELACOURT HERE!
DUANE? IT'S ZBIGGY! I NEED A HUMAN RIGHTS SYMBOL RIGHT AWAY!
GBTrudeau

GOOD EVENING. PRESIDENT CARTER'S NOMINEE FOR SECRETARY OF SYMBOLISM, DUANE DELACOURT, HAS GOTTEN OFF TO A RUNNING START.
SPEAKING AT A SPECIAL PRESS CONFERENCE LAST NIGHT, THE SECRETARY-DESIGNATE ANNOUNCED HE WOULD BE HOLDING REGULAR PHONE-A-THONS TO ASK AVERAGE AMERICANS WHAT SYMBOLS THEY WOULD MOST LIKE TO SEE IN THE CARTER ADMINISTRATION.
TODAY DUANE DELACOURT HELD HIS FIRST SUCH PHONE-A-THON AND NBC NEWS WAS THERE..
HELLO?
HELLO! THIS IS YOUR SECRETARY OF SYMBOLISM!
YEAH, I'D LIKE TO SEE MORE PHONE-A-THONS.
GBTrudeau

BOSS, I'M SORRY, BUT THE WORD I'M GETTING FROM THE HILL IS THAT THE SENATE JUST ISN'T GOING TO BUY A SECRETARY OF SYMBOLISM...
Jimmy
THE LIBERALS ARE STILL SORE ABOUT BELL, THE CONSERVATIVES ABOUT WARNKE. THEY'RE TIRED OF RUBBER-STAMPING!
RUBBER-STAMPING?! WHAT ABOUT SORENSEN?!
Jimmy
SORENSEN WITHDREW, SIR.
SO?
Jimmy
DOESN'T COUNT AS A KILL.
LOOK, WHAT IF I WALK UP TO THE HEARINGS WITH HIM?
Jimmy

"..AND THROUGH OUR PEOPLE PROGRAMS, WE HAVE ENCOURAGED THE AVERAGE AMERICAN TO DIRECTLY PARTICIPATE IN THE SYMBOL-MAKING PROCESS."
"THE PUBLIC RESPONSE THROUGH CALLS AND LETTERS HAS BEEN OVERWHELMINGLY FAVORABLE.."
SYMBOL-MAKING PROCESS?! YOU MUST BE JOKING!
MR. DELACOURT, WHEN WILL YOU PEOPLE LEARN THAT WHAT THIS COUNTRY NEEDS IS LESS PUBLIC RELATIONS AND MORE PUBLIC SERVICE!
"WROTE ONE 5-YEAR-OLD HANDICAPPED CHILD.."
I OBJECT! MR. CHAIRMAN, I OBJECT!
©BTrudeau

GOOD EVENING. TODAY, BY A NARROW MARGIN OF 50 TO 46, THE U.S. SENATE CONFIRMED DUANE DELACOURT AS THE NEW SECRETARY OF SYMBOLISM! CATHERINE MACKIN HAS MORE. CASSIE?
THANK YOU, JOHN. I'M HERE IN THE WHITE HOUSE BRIEFING ROOM WITH SECRETARY-ELECT DUANE DELACOURT. THE MOOD HERE IS ONE OF TRIUMPH, IS IT NOT, MR. SECRETARY?
YES. THAT'S RIGHT..
IT'S A MOMENT OF PERSONAL TRIUMPH, OF COURSE, BUT MORE IMPORTANTLY, IT IS A VICTORY FOR SYMBOLISM— FOR CARDIGANS, FOR TOWN MEETINGS, FOR CALL-IN SHOWS AND FOR FIRESIDE CHATS!
YES, IT'S A VICTORY FOR THE "LITTLE GUY," THE "MAN IN THE STREET," THE "AVERAGE JOE"!..
BACK TO YOU, JOHN, IF YOU DON'T MIND.
GBTrudeau

CYRUS? IT'S BRZEZINSKI.
HI, ZBIGGY! WHAT'S UP?
WELL, TODAY'S LIST OF FOREIGN POLICIES JUST CAME IN AND..
DON'T TELL ME—THEY'RE ALL FOR IMMEDIATE IMPLEMENTATION.
WELL, AS SOON AS WE CLARIFY THEM! I KNOW YOU'VE GOT A BACKLOG..
BACKLOG?! WE'RE GOING CRAZY OVER HERE! WHAT'S IT TODAY?
"1. A DEFENSIBLE HOMELAND FOR SOVIET DISSIDENTS.."
HOLD IT, LET ME GET A PENCIL..
Jim-Boy

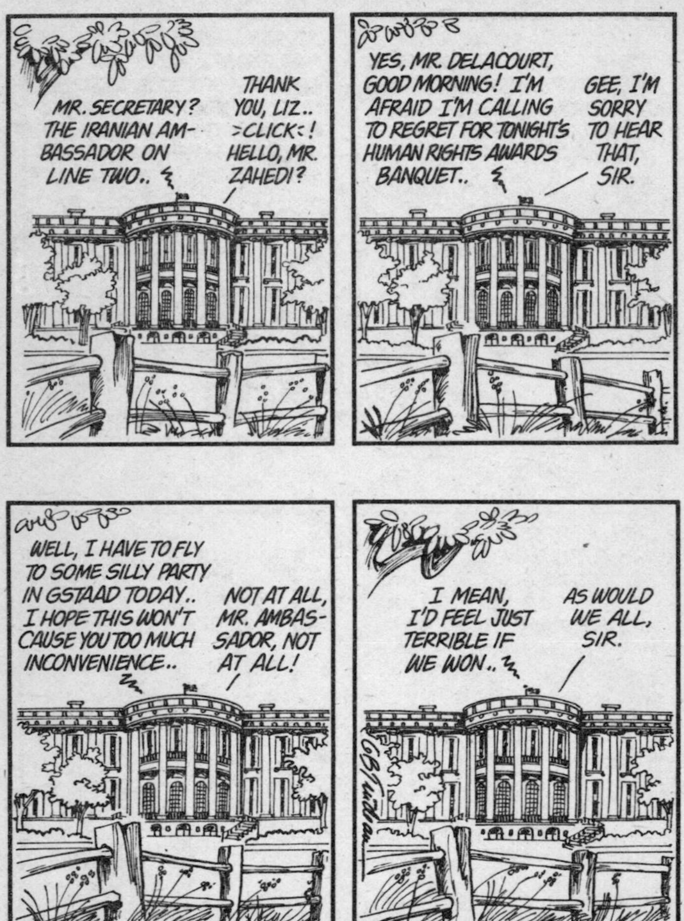
MR. SECRETARY? THE IRANIAN AMBASSADOR ON LINE TWO..
THANK YOU, LIZ.. >CLICK<! HELLO, MR. ZAHEDI?
YES, MR. DELACOURT, GOOD MORNING! I'M AFRAID I'M CALLING TO REGRET FOR TONIGHT'S HUMAN RIGHTS AWARDS BANQUET..
GEE, I'M SORRY TO HEAR THAT, SIR.
WELL, I HAVE TO FLY TO SOME SILLY PARTY IN GSTAAD TODAY.. I HOPE THIS WON'T CAUSE YOU TOO MUCH INCONVENIENCE..
NOT AT ALL, MR. AMBASSADOR, NOT AT ALL!
I MEAN, I'D FEEL JUST TERRIBLE IF WE WON..
AS WOULD WE ALL, SIR.

SAY, DOC, WE SURE WERE SURPRISED TO HEAR YOU WENT TO THE HUMAN RIGHTS BANQUET LAST WEEK!
YEAH, WE SURE WERE!
WELL, GENTLEMEN, NO REASONABLE PERSON CAN BE ADVERSE TO HONORING THOSE NATIONS WHICH RESPECT HUMAN RIGHTS. IT'S THE HYSTERICAL CRITICISM OF THOSE WHICH DON'T THAT IS SO COUNTERPRODUCTIVE!
DIALOGUE BETWEEN THE U.S. AND THE SOVIET UNION MUST PROCEED IN A CALM, NONCONFRONTATIONAL WAY, SO AS NOT TO PROVOKE ACCIDENTAL LINKAGE BETWEEN RIGHTS AND ARMS LIMITATIONS! DON'T YOU ALL AGREE?
UM.. IS THIS A QUIZ?
YES. YOU HAVE TEN MINUTES.
GBTrudeau

SIR, WHAT I DON'T GET IS WHY YOU HAD TO CONDUCT ALL THOSE NEGOTIATIONS IN SECRECY? WHY DIDN'T YOU JUST ANNOUNCE YOUR POSITIONS, LIKE MR. CARTER DOES?
AND GET MR. CARTER'S RESULTS? YOUNG MAN, I WAS NOT IN THE BUSINESS OF RHETORIC! A LASTING STRUCTURE OF PEACE WAS MY ONLY CONCERN!
AND WITH CONSTANT CONGRESSIONAL INTERFERENCE, YOU THINK THAT WAS EASY? YOU TRY SHAPING A NEW INTERNATIONAL ORDER!
UM.. WELL..
NO! DON'T DO IT, BARNEY! WE NEED YOU HERE AT HOME!
GBTrudeau

..AND UNDER THE FINAL VIETNAM SETTLEMENT, WE PROMISED WITHDRAWAL OF TROOPS, EQUAL ROLE FOR THE VIETCONG, AND A COMMITMENT TO POSTWAR RECONSTRUCTION AID!
SIR, COULD YOU EXPLAIN TO ME WHY YOU COULDN'T HAVE GOTTEN THE SAME TERMS IN 1969, THUS AVOIDING THE CARNAGE, ETC., OF THE NEXT FOUR YEARS?
BECAUSE UNTIL 1973, HANOI INSISTED ON SHARING POWER! WHAT A TOTALLY UNEDUCATED QUESTION! YOUNG MAN, WHERE DO YOU GET THESE IDEAS?!
UM.. BOOKS, MOSTLY..
WHO GAVE THEM TO YOU? WHO? OUT WITH IT!
I'LL HANDLE THIS, MR. WEIN-BURGER..
GBTrudeau

DR. KISSINGER, I REALIZE I HAVE THE BENEFIT OF HINDSIGHT, BUT..
MR. PERKINS! IF YOU PERSIST IN THESE OUTBURSTS, I'M GOING TO HAVE TO ASK YOU TO LEAVE!
LEAVE, SIR? ME?
NOW, HOLD ON THERE, DOC! LET'S NOT BE SO THIN-SKINNED! BARNEY HAS EARNED A PLACE IN THIS CLASS, AND YOU KNOW IT!
FOR WEEKS NOW, THIS BOY HAS BEEN POSING REASONABLE, GUILELESS QUESTIONS PERTAINING TO TRUTH IN FOREIGN POLICY! IN SO DOING, HE HAS BECOME THE **CONSCIENCE** OF THIS SEMINAR!
AND I FEEL COMFORTABLE IN THAT ROLE, SIR..
MOREOVER, HE'S THE ONLY ONE WHO DOES THE READING!
G B Trudeau

HEY, MARK!
WHY, MRS. DAVEN-PORT!
MARK! HOW NICE TO SEE YOU AGAIN, DEAR!
HEY, MARK! LOOK AT ME! I'M GLOWING!
DID YOUR HUSBAND COME THIS YEAR?
OH, YES! DICK WILL BE ALONG SHORTLY!
WANNA KNOW HOW I GOT THE EFFECT? DO YOU? HUH?
A DRINK, MRS. D.?
WASN'T THE GEN-TLEMAN HERE FIRST?
I TAPED A MINIATURE FLASHLIGHT TO MY NOSE! YUK! YUK!
THE GEN-TLEMAN WAS HERE TWO DAYS AGO.
OH. WELL, THEN I'LL HAVE A SHERRY!
GBTrudeau

HEY, JOANIE! HOW'S IT GOIN' BABE?
ZONKER?! WHERE ARE YOU?
RIGHT HERE IN LOTUS LAND! SCHOOL FINISHED LAST WEEK! WHAT'S UP WITH YOU?
WELL, I'M GOING TO GRADUATE! WANNA COME?
GRADUATE?! YOU MEAN... THEY'RE ABOUT TO MAKE YOU A.. A LAWYER?!
SOME-THING LIKE THAT.
HOLD ON, JOANIE! I'LL BE RIGHT OVER!
HEY, NO, I'M OKAY! I PROM-ISE!
GBTrudeau

NOW, JOANIE, WHAT'S ALL THIS NONSENSE ABOUT YOU ACTUALLY BECOMING A LAWYER?..
WELL, IT'S TRUE, ZONK! I'M GRADUATING FROM BOALT ON SATURDAY!
BUT, JOANIE, THAT'S..CRAZY! DO YOU HAVE ANY IDEA WHAT IT'S LIKE OUT THERE?
NO, NOT REALLY. BUT THAT'S WHY I'M LOOKING FORWARD TO IT SO MUCH..
ZONKER, IT'S TIME I STOPPED PREPARING FOR MY LIFE, AND STARTED GETTING ON WITH IT! I FEEL READY TO ACCEPT THE RESPONSIBILITY OF THE CHOICES I'VE MADE, TO FACE MY FUTURE SQUARELY!
EASY, JOANIE, EASY! YOU'RE BECOMING HYSTERICAL!
MY MIND'S MADE UP, ZONKER..
G.B. Trudeau

JOANIE, IS IT TOO LATE TO BLOW YOUR EXAMS?
ZONKER, I APPRECIATE YOUR CONCERN, BUT IT'S NO USE TRYING TO CHANGE MY MIND..
MAN, I JUST DON'T BELIEVE THIS! I MEAN, I KNOW A LOT OF PEOPLE WHO'VE TALKED ABOUT BECOMING LAWYERS, BUT NO ONE WHO ACTUALLY WENT THROUGH WITH IT!
ZONKER..
JOANIE, DOES RICK KNOW YET ABOUT YOUR GRADUATING FROM LAW SCHOOL?
OF COURSE, I DO!
AND YOU CONDONE IT?!
THE WORLD NEEDS GROWN-UPS, ZONKER.
GBTrudeau

IT'S BECAUSE I'M A WOMAN! THAT'S WHY, YOU KNOW! BECAUSE I'M A MIDDLE-AGED WOMAN, NO SCHOOL WILL EVER TAKE A CHANCE ON ME!
WALDEN
MY MANUAL! WHERE'S MY LAW SCHOOL MANUAL?.. OH, HERE IT IS.. STAMPS?. OH, AND MY YELLOW LEGAL PADS! HAVE I GOT ENOUGH? OOH, WHY IS LAW SCHOOL SO COMPLICATED?
KLM
GINNY, WHY AM I GOING TO LAW SCHOOL? WHAT IF IT DOESN'T WORK OUT? WHAT IF I'M BORED BY IT? WHAT IF I'M NO GOOD AT IT? WHAT IF I JUST CAN'T CUT THE MUSTARD!
©B Trudeau
MS. JOAN CAUCUS!
TA DA!

..AND, OF COURSE, IT'S VERY UPSETTING FOR ME PERSONALLY, MIKE. NONE OF MY FRIENDS HAS EVER GRADUATED BEFORE.
UH-HUH. WELL, HOW'S RICK FEEL, ZONK?
RICK? WELL, I'M NOT SURE..
I THINK HE'S STILL WAITING FOR HER TO CALM DOWN..
©B. Trudeau
YOU'RE BURSTING WITH PRIDE, AREN'T YOU, RICK?
GO TO SLEEP, JOANIE..

WHY, IT'S.. IT'S ADORABLE, RICK!
WELL, IT'S HOME..
AND THIS IS YOUR STUDY?
YEAH, SUCH AS IT IS.
OH, MY LORD! WHAT IS THAT, RICK?
I BELIEVE IT'S AN EGG SALAD SAND-WICH.
YOU RECOG-NIZE IT?
YEAH. SEE I LEFT IN KIND OF A HURRY LAST FALL..
GBTrudeau

MY DEAR, I WAS JUST SO PLEASED TO HEAR FROM YOU! YOU KNOW, I GREATLY ADMIRED THE WAY YOU HANDLED YOURSELF IN THE SLADE CAMPAIGN!
YOU DID?
ABSOLUTELY! NOW, LISTEN, MY ETHICS COMMITTEE IS GOING TO BE NEEDING NEW COUNSEL! WE'RE ABOUT TO HOLD HEARINGS ON..
THE KOREAN SCANDAL, YES, I KNOW!
OH, YOU DO! GOOD! DOES THAT SORT OF JOB INTEREST YOU AT ALL?
I'VE BEEN PREPARING FOR IT MY WHOLE LIFE.
HEAVENS! WELL, THEN I THINK YOU BETTER TAKE IT, DON'T YOU?
GBTrudeau

MY DEAR MS. CAUCUS! YOU ARE A WONDER! HARD AT WORK ALREADY!
THE CHIEF COUNSEL SENT ME DOWN HERE, LACEY. HE WANTS ME TO FAMILIARIZE MYSELF WITH SOME OF THE DOCUMENTARY EVI-DENCE!
WHAT DO YOU THINK SO FAR?
WELL, I'M JUST AMAZED! I HAD NO IDEA THERE WERE SO MANY REPUTATIONS AT STAKE!
THAT'S RIGHT. THAT'S WHY THE HEARINGS ARE SO SENSITIVE!
YOU KNOW, I CAN'T BELIEVE I'M FERRETING OUT CORRUP-TION ON MY FIRST DAY!
CAREFUL, NOW, DEAR! THAT'S FOR THE FEDS TO DECIDE.
GBTrudeau

TELL ME, ZONK, WHAT EXACTLY IS THE PERFECT TAN?
WELL, CORNELL, THE PERFECT TAN IS, OF COURSE, DIFFERENT THINGS TO DIFFERENT FOLKS..
BUT ACCORDING TO THE STANDARDS SET BY THE BAY AREA TAN TOURNEY, THE PERFECT TAN IS "A DEEP, HONEY-TONED GLOW ON ALL PARTS OF THE BODY NOT CLAD BY MODEST SWIMWEAR."
OF COURSE, SOME OF US ARE MORE THOROUGH THAN OTHERS. FOR INSTANCE, MOST PEOPLE DON'T BOTHER TO SPREAD THEIR TOES WITH BITS OF TOOTHPICKS!
WOW! WHAT ATTENTION TO DETAIL!
WELL, BELIEVE ME, IT PAYS OFF!
GBTrudeau

SO WHAT YOU BEEN UP TO, CORNELL?
WELL, MY OLD LADY AND I HAVE JUST BEEN THROUGH THE EST COURSE! BLEW US AWAY, MAN!
OH, YEAH, WHAT WAS THAT LIKE? I HEAR THAT WERNER'S SUPPOSED TO BE ONE HELLUVA TAP DANCER!
HE'S A LITTLE BIT MORE THAN THAT, ZONK!
IN LESS THAN 48 HOURS, HE TAUGHT US TO TAKE COMPLETE RE-SPONSIBILITY FOR OUR OWN LIVES, FOR EVERYTHING THAT HAPPENS TO US!
REALLY HAD YOU GOING, HUH?
NO, NO, IT WORKED! WE DECIDED TO SPLIT UP!
GB Trudeau

I DUNNO, CORNELL.. I'M NOT READY TO BUY THE EST LINE THAT ALL PROBLEMS CAN BE RESOLVED ATTITUDINALLY..
WERNER SAYS TO ANTICIPATE THAT REACTION AND TO ACCEPT IT!
WERNER SAYS ANY CRITICISM OF EST IS NOT A THREAT IF YOU'VE "GOT IT"!
HE DOES?
GOT WHAT? THE TUITION?
NO. "IT."
I DON'T GET IT.
WERNER KNOWS THAT, AND IT'S FINE WITH HIM.
GBTrudeau

SEE, CORNELL, EST IS ALL VERY FINE FOR MIDDLE-CLASS PILGRIMS.. YOU KNOW, FOLKS WHO HAVE ALL THE BASIC COMPONENTS FOR HAPPINESS, BUT STILL CAN'T GET IT TOGETHER..
BUT WHAT ABOUT THE MILLIONS OF DESTITUTE FOR WHOM EVERYDAY LIFE IS A CONSTANT ASSAULT ON HUMAN DIGNITY?
WHAT ABOUT THEM? THEY CAN'T AFFORD THE SEMINAR ANYWAY!
OH... YEAH.. THAT'S RIGHT..
WAIT A MINUTE! THAT'S MY POINT!
I ACCEPT YOUR HOSTILITY. DO YOU HAVE ANY BEER?
GB Trudeau

..AND I THANK MY CHINESE HOSTS FOR THEIR RELENTLESS HOSPITALITY!
(HE THANKS YOU FOR BEING HOSPITABLE.)
THE LAST YEAR HAS PASSED WITHOUT ANY MAJOR PROVOCATION AND I APPRECIATE THAT.
(HE THANKS YOU FOR BEING SO TOLERANT.)
I LOOK FORWARD TO MANY MORE YEARS OF WORKING WITH PEKING!
(HE DOESN'T KNOW YET HE'S BEING REPLACED BY LEONARD WOODCOCK.)
YOU'RE NOT PROJECTING, HONEY.
(HE DOESN'T KNOW YET HE'S BEING REPLACED BY LEONARD WOODCOCK!)
G B Trudeau

I'M SORRY TO BE THE ONE TO TELL YOU, SIR, I..
WOODCOCK?! LEONARD WOODCOCK IS REPLACING ME?!
I KNEW IT! I KNEW CARTER WAS A FRAUD! ONCE AGAIN, THE POLS PLAY PORK BARREL, AND A TOP FLIGHT CAREER DIPLOMAT IS OUT ON THE STREET!
WELL, THEY WON'T GET AWAY WITH IT, DO YOU HEAR ME?! THEY WON'T GET AWAY WITH IT!
YOU HAVE A PLAN, SIR?
A PLAN.. YOU'RE RIGHT! I'LL NEED A PLAN!
GBTrudeau

HONEY, YOU MUST HAVE YOUR STORIES MIXED UP! CY WOULD NEVER RECALL ME! I'M INDI-SPENSABLE, AND HE KNOWS IT!
I MEAN, LOOK AT MY RECORD HERE! I TOOK A SHABBY EM-BASSY GOLF COURSE, AND TURNED IT INTO A **MAGNIFICENT** RIFLE RANGE! I **LED** THE WAY IN MAKING COKE AN **ACCEPTED** APERITIF AT PEKING SOCIAL FUNC-TIONS!
HELL, I WAS EVEN THE FIRST GRINGO TO GET **STONED** ON THE **GREAT WALL**!
ARE YOU SURE, SIR?
OH.. RIGHT.. WHAT WAS IT NIXON KEPT SAYING?
"IT IS INDEED A GREAT WALL." WE HAD TO WONDER.
GB Trudeau

LEONARD WOODCOCK! I JUST CAN'T GET OVER IT! WHAT EVER COULD HAVE POSSESSED CARTER TO PICK WOODCOCK FOR CHINA?
WELL, SIR, MAYBE IT'S BECAUSE MR. WOODCOCK'S CAREER HAS BEEN ONE OF GREAT SENSITIVITY TO THE PLIGHT OF THE WORKING CLASS!
HONEY, ALL LABOR LEADERS ARE SENSITIVE TO THE WORKING CLASS! THAT'S HOW THEY AVOID BELONGING TO IT!
BUT DIDN'T HE TAKE ON THE GANG OF THREE, SIR?
THAT'S THE BIG THREE! AND NEXT TO YOU PEOPLE, THOSE GUYS ARE PUSSY-CATS!
GBTrudeau

WHAT'S IT SAY, DAD? IS SOMEBODY SICK?
NO, IT'S FROM DUKE! HE'S COMING IN TODAY!
SEED
UNCLE DUKE? WHY ISN'T HE AT HIS POST IN CHINA?
GUESS HE WAS RELIEVED..
SEED
DARN! WHAT A TIME FOR HIM TO COME VISITING! RIGHT IN THE MIDDLE OF MY TANNING PROGRAM!
BUT HE IS YOUR UNCLE, SON. COULDN'T YOU TAKE A FEW DAYS OFF?
SEED
ARE YOU KIDDING? AND RISK PEELING?!
CAN'T YOU GO ON EMOLLIENTS?
SEED
GBTrudeau

ZONKER? YOUR UNCLE DUKE IS HERE!
YES, DAD?
UM.. WELL, HE'LL HAVE TO WAIT, DAD. I'M RIGHT IN THE MIDDLE OF A TAN MAINTENANCE SESSION.
SORRY, SON. I ALREADY SENT HIM BACK.
HI, THERE, NEPHEW!
WELL, HEY! UNCLE DUKE! LONG TIME, MAN!
YUP. TWO YEARS. PLEASE—DON'T GET UP.
FORGIVE ME, DUKE. YOU'VE COME AT AN AWKWARD TIME.
GBTrudeau

I DUNNO, NEPHEW, MAYBE WHAT I NEED IS A RESUME!
UNCLE DUKE, WHAT YOU REALLY NEED IS A GOOD TAN!
YOU MAY SCOFF, BUT I'M HERE TO TELL YOU THAT IF YOU'RE WEARING A GOOD TAN, ALL YOUR PROBLEMS BECOME LIKE SNOW IN THE NOON DAY SUN!
I DON'T GET IT. WHY ARE YOU SO SOLD ON RAYS?
THE MYSTIQUE, MOSTLY. THERE'S VERY LITTLE IN THIS WORLD THAT'S AS PROFOUND AS A DEEP, RICH TAN!
WHY CAN'T YOU GET INTERESTED IN BASEBALL OR DRUGS LIKE OTHER BOYS YOUR AGE?
DUKE, I WON'T APOLOGIZE FOR CARING ABOUT MY PERSONAL APPEARANCE!
GBTrudeau